MY DOG GOT NO NOSE!

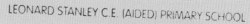

A play by
Steve Barlow and Steve Skidmore

Illustrated by Steve May

Characters

Ben

Andy

Emma

Rashid

Kirsty

Laura

3

A school playground at breaktime. Children are standing around chatting. Ben is telling jokes to Andy. Emma is listening too.

Ben: Here, Andy. Listen to this, listen to this! My dog's got no nose.

Andy: How does he smell?

Ben: Terrible!

Andy: What?

Ben: He smells terrible!

Andy: Why? Is he ill?

Ben: No! I said, he's got no nose!

Emma: So?

Ben: What do you mean, 'so'?

Emma: Well, if he's got no nose, he wouldn't be able to smell anything.

Ben: Right!

Emma: Yes – but that wouldn't make **him** smell terrible.

Ben: No, look – it's a joke.

Andy: I don't get it.

Emma: Me neither.

Ben: Oh, forget it. Kirsty! Kirsty, come over here. You too, Laura.

Kirsty: What do you want, Ben?

Ben: Listen – my dog's got no nose.

Laura: Aaaah! Poor little thing.

Ben: What?

Laura: Well, he won't be able to smell anything, will he?

Ben: No, listen …

Kirsty: How would you like it, if you were a dog and you couldn't smell anything?

Ben: Yes, but …

Emma: Hey, Rashid! Guess what!

Rashid: What?

Emma: Ben's dog's got no nose.

Laura: Yes, just imagine how awful it must be!

Kirsty: It's terrible!

Rashid: You're right! A sense of smell is very important to a dog.

Andy: I saw that on TV. This woman was training dogs. She said that dogs can't see as many colours as us but they can smell all sorts of stuff that we can't ...

Ben: Just a minute ...

8

Kirsty: That's right, so if a dog hasn't got a nose, it's almost like being blind.

Laura: Yes, or like being deaf ...

Rashid: How come your dog's got no nose anyway, Ben? What happened to its nose?

Ben: What do you mean, what happened to it?

Rashid: Well, did it just stop working? Or was it an accident?

Ben: An accident?

Laura: Good point, Rashid! Did its nose get run over by a car, or caught in a door or something?

Rashid: Or maybe it ran nose-first into a tree?

Ben: No!

Laura: Because if it did, maybe my mum could help. She's a vet.

Ben: Look, there's nothing wrong with the dog.

Kirsty: That's not what you told us.

Laura: You said it had no nose.

Andy: And you told me it smelled terrible, as well.

Emma: Sounds like it definitely needs to see a vet.

Kirsty: Yes, you've got to get it to the vet at once, Ben!

Ben: Aaargh! Listen ...

Rashid: No, **you** listen, Ben. Your dog's really ill, but you won't take it to the vet.

Kirsty: That's animal cruelty, that is! When your pet's ill, you have to take it to the vet.

Ben: But it's not ...

Emma: You can't neglect a poor animal that can't look after itself.

Rashid: No! You're the owner – it's your job to look after it!

Laura: You'll have the RSPCA round. That's what my dad says. He says people that don't look after their pets shouldn't be allowed to have them.

Emma: My mum says people who hurt animals should be sent to prison. Especially donkeys.

Kirsty: What, donkeys who hurt animals should be sent to prison?

Emma: No, people who hurt donkeys should be sent to prison. My mum likes donkeys.

Ben: I haven't hurt any animals ...

Andy: I've just had a thought. What sort of dog is it?

Ben: What sort of dog?

Andy: Yes, I mean, is it a German Shepherd dog or a Jack Russell terrier? What breed is it?

Ben: It doesn't matter what breed it is!

Andy: Yes it does! If it's a bulldog, it probably doesn't smell very well anyway, because its nose is all scrunched up.

Rashid: Yeah, but bloodhounds have a very strong sense of smell.

Kirsty: That's right! They help the police to track criminals and stuff.

Laura: Ooh, yes, it would be terrible for a bloodhound if it had no nose.

Emma: Or a sniffer dog.

Rashid: What do you mean, a sniffer dog?

Emma: You know – they find people buried in earthquakes and all sorts of stuff.

Kirsty: Or what about foxhounds? How would they cope without a nose? All hounds need a good sense of smell, really.

Rashid: Not greyhounds, though.

Andy: Why not greyhounds?

Rashid: Well, they have to chase an electric hare round a track.

Laura: So?

Rashid: Well, a greyhound with a really good sense of smell could tell that it wasn't a real hare, just a fake one, so it wouldn't bother to run.

Andy: I see what you mean. It would lose every race ...

Ben: Just listen, everyone! There isn't any dog!

Laura: What?

Emma: Then why did you say there was?

Kirsty: Were you lying to us, Ben?

21

Ben: It's just a joke! Okay? There's nothing wrong with my dog. I don't even have a dog!

Andy: Then why did you tell us you did?

Ben: Oh, why did I start this? Look, this is how it works. Andy, let's try it again, and listen this time. Right? I say – my dog's got no nose.

Andy: Your dog's got no nose?

Ben: How does he smell?

Andy: Terrible. I've heard it.

Kirsty: We've all heard it, Ben. We were just winding you up.

Laura: It's a rotten joke anyway.

The school bell rings.

Emma: That's the end of break. Come on – it's topic work next.

Rashid: Maybe we'll be doing noses.

Ben: Who knows – knows, nose – get it? Ha ha!

Others: Oh no! Not another joke …

Ben: Do you know the trouble with you lot? You've got no sense of humour!